Rock Jaw
Master of the Eastern Border

OTHER **BONE** BOOKS

ROCK JAW
Master of the Eastern Border

BY JEFF SMITH
WITH COLOR BY STEVE HAMAKER

An Imprint of

■SCHOLASTIC

New York   Toronto   London   Auckland   Sydney   Mexico City   New Delhi   Hong Kong   Buenos Aires

Library of Congress Catalog Card Number 95068403.

ISBN-13 978-0-439-70627-8 — ISBN-10 0-439-70627-0 (hardcover)

ISBN 0-439-70636-X (paperback)

ACKNOWLEDGMENTS

Harvestar Family Crest designed by Charles Vess

Map of *The Valley* by Mark Crilley

Color by Steve Hamaker

12 11 10 9   10 11 12/0

First Scholastic edition, February 2007

Book design by David Saylor

Printed in Singapore 46

This book is for Krishna and Avaday Iyer

CONTENTS

GO ON!! GET LOST!!! WE DON'T WANT YOU AROUND HERE!

OKAY! OKAY! THEY'RE GONE!

DID YOU SEE **THAT**, FONE BONE? HE **SAVED** US! YOU **SAVED** US, BARTLEBY! OH, **BOY!** EVERYTHING'S GONNA BE **ACES** FROM NOW ON!

HMM.

WHAT'S THE **MATTER**, CUZ? EVERYTHING'S GONNA BE **ACES** FROM NOW ON, **RIGHT?** HE **SAVED US!**

WELL . . .

PAT PAT

THE WHOLE REASON WE CAME **UP** HERE WAS TO GIVE BARTLEBY BACK TO THE **RAT CREATURES**, AND LOOK WHAT **HAPPENED!**

YEAH. THAT DIDN'T WORK OUT TOO GOOD, DID IT?

NOW I DON'T KNOW **WHAT** WE'RE DOIN'.

AT THE MOMENT, YOU ARE **TRESPASSING.**

WE, UH... WHO'S THEM?

WHO'S HIM?

COME, COME...

YOU KNOW...

...THEM! THE OLD COW WOMAN AND THE DRAGONS.

...OR HIM.

SURELY YOU KNOW OF HIM -- THE MASTER OF THE RAT CREATURES -- THE HOODED ONE!

GULP!

THE VALLEY IS DIVIDED IN TWO...

EVERYONE MUST CHOOSE A SIDE!

WHY?

WE'RE STRANGERS IN THE VALLEY-- ALL WE WANT TO DO IS RETURN THIS LOST CUB BACK TO HIS HOME IN THE MOUNTAINS, MISTER-- UH... MISTER--?

I AM **ROQUE JA,** MASTER OF THE EASTERN BORDER. EVERYTHING YOU SEE IN THESE MOUNTAINS BELONGS TO **ME.**

HISS!

ANYTHING THAT **MOVES** IN MY DOMAIN, DOES SO ONLY WITH MY **LEAVE...**

AND THAT **INCLUDES** RAT CREATURES!

OKAY, OKAY, MR. ROCK JAW! WE DON'T WANT TO MESS WITH YOUR **DOMAIN--** WE JUST WANNA TAKE TH' KID **HOME!**

SO, YOU ARE **STRANGERS** IN OUR VALLEY...

YEAH, WE'RE--

..UH..

HOW **INTERESTING.**

FONE BONE! WE DON'T **LIKE** THIS GUY...

BONE, DID YOU SAY?

THE HOODED ONE IS **SEARCHING** FOR SOMEONE NAMED **BONE...**

HE IS?

YES. THE ONE WHO BEARS THE **STAR** IS NAMED **BONE.**

DO YOU **KNOW** HIM, PERHAPS?

A **STAR**? HEY! I THINK HE MEANS **PHONEY BONE**! WHAT'S HE WANT WITH **HIM**?

YEAH! HOLD IT RIGHT THERE, ROCK JAW!

R-R-ROQUE JA! R-R-ROQUE! YOU'RE NOT ROLLING THE **R**!

WHAT'S THIS HOODED GUY WANT WITH OUR COUSIN?

THE VALLEY IS **DIVIDED**, YOU SEE, EVER SINCE THE FALL OF THE KINGDOM, AND THE HOODED ONE SEES IT AS RIPE FOR **PLUCKING**.

BUT HE FEARS THAT A NEW **LEADER** WILL ARISE AND **UNITE THE VALLEY** BEFORE HE CAN **CONQUER** IT.

HOWEVER, IF YOUR COUSIN LOOKS ANYTHING LIKE **YOU TWO**, I HARDLY THINK HE'LL BE A **THREAT**!

ARE YOU TELLIN' ME THAT THE HOODED ONE THINKS **PHONEY BONE** IS GONNA **UNITE THE VALLEY**?

HA!

PHONEY'S NO **LEADER**! HE GOT CHASED OUT OF **BONEVILLE** JUST FOR SAYIN' HE WANTED TO RUN FOR **MAYOR**!

THAT'S ENOUGH, SMILEY. WHO'S SIDE ARE **YOU** ON, ROCK JAW?

TWO BONES AND A RUNAWAY **RAT CREATURE.**

I IMAGINE THERE WILL BE A SIZABLE **REWARD** FOR BRINGING THE THREE OF YOU IN. . . .

BUT I DON'T WANT ANY MORE **DIFFICULTIES,** SO SEND THE **CUB** UP FIRST.

YOU'RE NOT GONNA SEPARATE **US!**

THE CUB. **NOW.**

FORGET IT! YOU'LL NEVER GET THIS **CUB!**

ERF.....

GO ON AN' LEAVE US ALONE! WE DIDN'T DO ANYTHING TO YOU!

SNIFF.

I MISS MY MOMMA.

NOW LOOK WHAT YOU'VE DONE!

HEY, I DIDN'T EAT HIS FOLKS!

C'MON! I SAY WE TEACH THOSE RATS A **LESSON!**

BUT WHAT CAN WE DO? THEY'RE SO MUCH **BIGGER** THAN WE ARE!

WE CAN FIND **FONE BONE** AND **SMILEY!** THEY'LL HELP US!

WE WERE ON THEIR TRAIL **ANYWAY!** THEY CAN'T BE THAT FAR!

LET'S GO!

HOLD UP!

HOLD UP!

WHAT THE **HECK?**

...YOU SHOULD WORRY ABOUT YOUR **OWN** POSITION, MR. BONE.

IT WILL BE MUCH **EASIER** FOR YOU IN THE END IF YOU JUST **CHOOSE** A SIDE.

YEAH, YEAH.

PAT!

HEY!

WHAT WAS **THAT** FOR, ROCK JAW?

I THOUGHT I TOLD YOU NOT TO WALK ON THE SAME **SIDE** AS THE RAT CREATURE CUB.

IS THAT ALL YOU **THINK** ABOUT? SIDES?

THERE **IS** A WAR GOING ON. YOU WILL **NEED** TO **CHOOSE** A SIDE!

NOT EVERYONE WANTS TO **CHOOSE** SIDES, YA KNOW!

SO BACK OFF!

RIGHT! THERE MIGHT BE **OTHER** SIDES THAT WE WANT TO **CONSIDER!**

SUCH AS **INSIDE** VERSUS **OUTSIDE?**

WHOOP!

I'M MORE AN **OUT-DOORSY** TYPE, MYSELF!

HOW **RUGGED** OF YOU.

I GUESS THAT DEPENDS ON WHOSE SIDE YOUR **FRIENDS** ARE ON.

WHOSE SIDE?

ROQUE JA SAYS EVERYBODY HAS TO BE ON A SIDE NOW BECAUSE IT'S A **WAR.** YOU CAN EITHER PICK THE **RAT CREATURES** OR THE **DRAGONS.**

I PICK THE **DRAGONS** . . .

. . . I'VE NEVER **SEEN** A **DRAGON**, BUT I KNOW I DON'T LIKE THOSE **RAT CREATURES!**

WELL, WE'RE NOT ON THE RAT CREATURES' SIDE **EITHER!**

BUT WHOSE SIDE IS **HE** ON?

ROQUE JA?

EVERYBODY KNOWS ROQUE JA **HATES** DRAGONS – –

UH, OH!

I THINK THE **BONE COUSINS** ARE IN **TROUBLE!**

IF YOU'RE NOT TOO FAT AN' LAZY TO CATCH US, THAT IS!

SSSS!

HOLD IT!

THEY'RE JUST TRYING TO GET A RISE OUT OF YOU, COMRADE! BESIDES, THEY ARE LITTLE AND MUCH TOO QUICK FOR US! WE WILL HAVE TO OUTWIT THEM!

WHAT'S TH' MATTER? I THOUGHT YOU WERE MEAT EATERS, NOT QUICHE-EATING OLD LADIES!

!

WHO ARE YOU CALLING QUICHE-EATING OLD LADIES?!

NOW? SHALL WE OUTWIT THEM NOW?

COME BACK HERE, YOU LITTLE BRAT! I'LL SHOW YOU WHO'S A QUICHE-EATING OLD LADY!!

WAHOO!

YES! COME BACK! WE'LL OUTWIT YOU TO DEATH!

IF YOU DON'T LIKE RAT CREATURES SO MUCH, WHY DON'T YOU TEAM UP WITH THE **DRAGONS** AND CHASE THEM OFF?

BECAUSE THE ONLY THING **WORSE** THAN THE RAT CREATURES ARE THOSE ARROGANT **DRAGONS!**

DO YOU KNOW WHAT THE **VALLEY PEOPLE** THINK ABOUT THE DRAGONS? THEY THINK THE DRAGONS **CREATED THE VALLEY!!**

SO?

SO, THEY THINK THE **QUEEN** OF THE DRAGONS WENT **MAD** ONE DAY, AND ALL THE OTHER DRAGONS WERE FORCED TO COME AND **RESTRAIN** HER . . .

SHE RESISTED, AND OUR LANDSCAPE IS THE RESULT OF THEIR **BATTLE** - - THEY CRASHED AND PUSHED AGAINST THE **MOUNTAINS**, AND CREATED THE **VALLEY**. IN THE END, WHEN THEY COULD NOT **STOP** HER, THEY HAD TO TURN HER TO **STONE!**

IF YOU ASK ME, IT'S A FOOLISH **FAIRY TALE** FIT ONLY FOR THE WEAK-MINDED.

DID YOU SAY SHE WAS TURNED TO **STONE?**

HEY!

HERE, KITTY KITTY KITTY!

!

SKRITCH!

WATCH IT. WE'RE IN SOME HUGE OPEN SPACE NOW.

SKRITCH

JUST A LITTLE FARTHER! WE'RE ALMOST THERE!

I HOPE SO. IT'S GETTIN' A LITTLE **STUFFY** IN HERE.

THIS IS IT, SMILEY! THIS IS THE **OPENING!** I'M OUTSIDE!

WHOA.

NOW **THERE'S** SOMETHIN' YOU DON'T SEE EVERY DAY!

YEAH, BOY.

HEY, SMILEY...

...YOU REMEMBER WHEN WE WERE WITH **ROCK JAW**, HE TOLD US A STORY ABOUT HOW THE VALLEY WAS CREATED?

YEAH, I REMEMBER. A BUNCH OF **DRAGONS** HAD A **FIGHT** AN' PUSHED UP THE MOUNTAINS.

RIGHT! THE QUEEN OF THE DRAGONS WENT MAD AND STARTED ON A **RAMPAGE!** THE **REST** OF THE DRAGONS WERE TRYING TO STOP HER!

AND TH' ONLY WAY THEY COULD **DO** IT WAS TO **TURN HER TO STONE!**

YOU MEAN...

THIS IS THE **QUEEN OF THE DRAGONS TURNED TO STONE?!**

NO, NO, NO! THIS ISN'T TH' **QUEEN!** THIS IS JUST AN ANCIENT **TEMPLE** OF SOME KIND -- *

UM. AT LEAST I **THINK** IT'S JUST AN ANCIENT TEMPLE...

LISTEN, SMILEY! BEING **TURNED TO STONE** IS THE SAME THING THAT HAPPENED TO **ANOTHER** ANCIENT ENEMY OF THE DRAGONS! THE **SAME** ENEMY WHO IS AFTER **PHONEY BONE** AND **THORN!**

BUT I THOUGHT IT WAS A **FAIRY TALE** AN' NOBODY **BELIEVED** IN DRAGONS ANYMORE!

WE KNOW **SOME** PEOPLE WHO BELIEVE IN THEM -- LIKE **GRAN'MA BEN** AND **LUCIUS DOWN!** I'VE SEEN A DRAGON, **TOO,** REMEMBER?

THE **LORD OF THE LOCUSTS** IS AFTER PHONEY BONE AND THORN, AND **HE** WAS AN ANCIENT ENEMY OF THE DRAGONS **WHO WAS TURNED TO STONE!**

YOU MEAN TH' **QUEEN OF THE DRAGONS** AND **THE LORD OF THE LOCUSTS** ARE ONE AND THE SAME?

COULD BE. I DON'T KNOW. IT'S A WEIRD COINCIDENCE, ANYWAY.

SO . . . ? IS THIS JUST A TEMPLE OR **NOT?**

PRETTY SURE IT'S JUST A **TEMPLE!** MAYBE IT'S AN OLD **RAT CREATURE** TEMPLE. . .

IN ANY CASE, IT LOOKS **ABANDONED** NOW.

YEAH, YOU'RE RIGHT! IT'S JUST SOME OLD **ABANDONED BUILDING!** BESIDES, EVEN IF IT **WAS** AN OL' ENEMY OF TH' DRAGONS, HOW CAN IT HURT YOU IF IT'S TURNED TO **STONE?**

SAY, WHERE'D THE KIDS GO?

HEY, FONE BONE AND SMILEY BONE! **OVER HERE!**

WE'RE NOT OUT OF DANGER YET! RODERICK SAYS WE WON'T BE SAFE UNTIL WE REACH THE TREE LINE!

ONCE WE'RE IN TH' FOREST **NO ONE** CAN FIND US!

WHAT'S **ROCK JAW** UP TO?

HE'S STILL WATCHING THE UPPER ENTRANCE!

BUT HE'S STARTING TO GET **SUSPICIOUS!**

WE BETTER GET GOING.

IT'S A PRETTY STEEP CLIFF, BUT IT'S THE ONLY WAY DOWN FROM HERE, SO YOU **BIG GUYS** WILL JUST HAVE TO BE **CAREFUL!**

DON'T WORRY ABOUT US! WE CAN HANDLE IT!

LET'S GO!

THIS ISN'T SO STEEP!

WE'RE NOT TO THE **STEEP** PART, YET!

HEY, FONE BONE, HOW YOU COMIN' WITH YER **LOVE POEMS?**

MM?

HEY! HEY! I DON'T WANNA TALK ABOUT **THAT** IN FRONT OF EVERYBODY!

YOU WRITE **LOVE POEMS**, MR. BONE?

uh...

C'MON, BONE! TELL US A **LOVE POEM!**

YES! A LOVE POEM THAT YOU WROTE FOR MISS **THORN!**

WHAT MAKES YOU THINK MY LOVE POEMS ARE FOR **THORN?**

AW, HECK, BONE! EVERYONE **KNOWS** THEY'RE FOR **THORN!** JEEZ!

I'D LIKE TO HEAR A LOVE POEM, MR. BONE!

ME, TOO!

SURE! WE ALL WOULD!

FORGET IT! YOU'LL **LAUGH!**

YOU'RE FROM TH' MOUNTAINS, RODERICK! WHERE'S TH' VILLAGE OF **BARRELHAVEN** FROM HERE?

I'VE NEVER **HEARD** OF BARRELHAVEN BEFORE. SORRY.

WHAT DO YOU THINK, FONE? I MEAN WE **DID** LEAVE **PHONEY BONE** IN THE VILLAGE. YOU DON'T THINK ANYTHING COULD HAVE **HAPPENED** WHILE WE'VE BEEN AWAY?

HMM.

I THINK WE BETTER GET DOWN THERE.

SHOW US WHERE TO GO, KIDS.

WELL, WELL . . . IF IT ISN'T THE BONE COUSINS!

. . . AND THE LITTLE SNOTS WHO PUSHED US **OFF THE CLIFF!**

OH, NO! NOT **AGAIN!**

HEH, HEH, EXCEPT **THIS** TIME, THERE IS NO GIANT **MOUNTAIN LION** AROUND TO INTERFERE!

YESSS! **ROGUE JA** IS STILL KEEPING WATCH ON YOUR LITTLE **MOUSEY HOLE** UP ABOVE!

I AM NOT **INTERESTED** IN BARGAINING FOR THEIR **MEANINGLESS** LIVES!

YOU ALL WILL

DIE--

UNLESS . . .

UNLESS WHAT?

. . . UNLESS YOU TELL ME THE WHEREABOUTS OF **THE ONE WHO BEARS THE STAR!**

THE CHOICE IS **YOURS** . . .

DECIDE **QUICKLY!** MY PATIENCE IS **RUNNING OUT!**

THE ONE WHO BEARS THE STAR? THAT'S THE SAME NAME **ROCK JAW** USED FOR **PHONEY BONE!** WHY IS EVERYBODY AFTER OUR **COUSIN?!**

THEY THINK PHONEY WANTS TO BE LEADER OF THE **VALLEY,** REMEMBER?

WHATEVER YOU CALL IT, IT LEAVES ONLY **ONE** WAY OUT! FORWARD!

BUT-- BUT WE DON'T KNOW WHERE TH' LEDGE **GOES!**

YES! WHAT IF IT TAKES US RIGHT TO **KINGDOK?**

OR BACK TO **ROCK JAW,** THE GIANT MOUNTAIN LION! DON'T FORGET ABOUT **HIM!**

WHAT CHOICE DO WE HAVE?

HOLD ON--

HEY, BIRD KIDS! CAN YOU SEE WHERE THIS LEDGE GOES?

THE LEDGE GETS **SMALLER** AND **SMALLER!**

BUT FARTHER AHEAD IS A **BOULDER FLOW!** IF YOU CAN REACH IT, YOU MIGHT BE ABLE TO WORK YOUR WAY DOWN TO THE TREES!

THIS IS **INSANE!**

IT'S **STUPID!**

HEY! NOTHING WE'VE DONE SO FAR HAS BEEN **UN-STUPID,** AND WE'RE STILL **ALIVE,** AREN'T WE?!

I CAN'T REALLY **ARGUE** WITH THAT, BUT I FEEL LIKE I **SHOULD.**

CARRY ON, FONE BONE! MAKE A **STUPID DECISION!**

RIGHT! FOLLOW ME!

WHAT HAPPENED?!

SOMETHING FELL OUT OF BONE'S **BACKPACK** AND SCARED OFF THE LOCUSTS!

WHERE'S KINGDOK?

HE DISAPPEARED!

Poof! VANISHED INTO THIN AIR!

UUHN!

IS HE OKAY?

OW OOW.

MAN! I FELL ON THE **EXACT** SAME SPOT THAT JUST **HEALED!**

HEY! WHAT HAPPENED TO THE **LOCUSTS?**

SOMETHING IN YOUR BACKPACK SCARED THEM OFF! ARE YOU **OKAY?**

WHOA! **CHECK IT OUT!**

IT LOOKS LIKE A **CROWN!**

OOH!

A **CROWN!** I BET IT BELONGS TO **THORN!**

WHAT'RE YOU DOING WITH **THAT** IN YOUR **BACKPACK,** CUZ?

I HAD NO **IDEA** WHAT WAS IN THAT BUNDLE! **GRAN'MA BEN** GAVE IT TO ME AND ASKED ME TO KEEP IT **SAFE!**

WHAT **ELSE** IS IN THERE?

A GLOVE; SOME KINDA METAL **SHIRT . . .**

?

AND **THIS!** AN OLD **MEDALLION!**

HISS!

SSSS!

PUT IT AWAY!

WHAT'S THE MATTER?

THE MEDALLION! PUT IT **AWAY!**

IT IS A **BAD** THING!

HISS!

PUT IT AWAY, SMILEY.

OKAY, OKAY!

THAT IS WHAT SCARED THE **LOCUSTS** AWAY! IT IS A **DRAGON-**THING!

A DREAMING-THING!

A DREAMING-THING?

DREAMING IS PART OF THE LOCAL **BELIEF SYSTEM.** GRAN'MA BEN WAS TELLING ME ABOUT IT.

YOU MEAN IT'S A **RELIGION?**

IT'S A RELIGION FOR **GRAN'MA BEN** AND **THORN!**

DREAMING IS A **PEOPLE** WORD.! ANIMALS CALL IT **HUM-HUM!** IT'S THE HUM OF THE EARTH!

THE EARTH **HUMS?**

OF COURSE IT DOES! WHAT A **RIDICULOUS QUESTION!** DON'T YOU **HEAR** IT?

MMMMMM NOPE. SORRY.

AW, **C'MON!** YOU **GOTTA** HEAR IT! HOW ELSE COULD YOU LEARN TO **WALK,** OR TALK OR FIND **FOOD** FOR YOURSELF?!

IF I DIDN'T LEARN IT IN TH' **FOURTH GRADE,** IT DIDN'T NEED **LEARNIN'!**

hmmf.

I HATE TO **BREAK IT UP,** GUYS, BUT WE CAN'T STAY HERE. WE'RE NOT **SAFE** UNTIL WE MAKE IT TO THE **TREES!**

WHAT ABOUT **YOU,** BONE? DO YOU HEAR IT?

WELL, ACTUALLY, WHERE **WE** COME FROM THERE IS NO **HUM-HUM** SO - -

THAT'S NOT **TRUE!** IT'S EVERYWHERE! IT'S **STRONGER** IN SOME PLACES, BUT IT'S **EVERYWHERE!**

HE'S **RIGHT!**

DIDN'T YOU FEEL IT BACK AT THE **OLD STONE TEMPLE?**

OH, MAN, THE **HUM-HUM'S** ALWAYS CRAZY AT THE OLD TEMPLE, BUT TODAY IT WAS **SCARY!**

NO KIDDING! THAT WHOLE **KINGDOK** THING WAS **INTENSE!**

YEAH! DIDN'T HE LOOK **REAL?** I THOUGHT HE **WAS** REAL, UNTIL HE VANISHED!

?

YOU MEAN HE **WASN'T** REAL?

OH, MY **GOSH!** YOU THINK KINGDOK WAS PART OF A **DREAM?!**

OH, YEAH, FOR **SURE!** SOMETIMES WHEN YOU GO THROUGH THE TEMPLE YOU GET **NIGHTMARES!**

WHOA, WHOA.

ARE YOU SAYING KINGDOK **WASN'T** EVEN THERE?! WE JUST **DREAMED** IT?

YEAH! SEE? **THAT'S** HUM-HUM!

NOW JUST **HOLD ON --** WHAT ABOUT ALL TH' **ROCKS** THAT WERE CRASHING DOWN **AROUND** US? THE **LEDGE** CRUMBLING OUT FROM UNDER OUR FEET?

THINGS GET **CRAZY** AROUND THAT OLD TEMPLE!

FOLKS SAY IT WAS BUILT ON A **GHOST CIRCLE!**

I BET IF WE WENT **BACK,** THE LEDGE WOULD BE **IN ONE PIECE!**

OH, COME **ON!** WE **SAW** IT -- WE **FELT** IT!

YOU CAN FEEL STUFF WHEN YOU **DREAM!**

!

MAN!

WHAT DID YOU SAY THIS TEMPLE WAS BUILT ON?

A **GHOST CIRCLE!** THAT'S WHERE THE LOCUSTS COME FROM.

VERY DANGEROUS! IF YOU STEP INTO ONE YOU'LL **DISAPPEAR!**

YOU GUYS ARE **SERIOUS!**

COOL!

SMILEY, THE GUY WHO'S AFTER **PHONEY BONE** -- -- HE'S CALLED THE LORD OF THE **LOCUSTS!**

RIGHT, RIGHT! HE PROBABLY CONTROLS THE **LOCUSTS!** HENCE TH' **NAME!**

I STILL DON'T UNDERSTAND HOW HE COULD INDUCE A **MASS HALLUCINATION** LIKE THAT.

MAYBE WE SHOULD GO BACK AND MAKE SURE PHONEY'S **OKAY.**

THIS GUY IS AFTER **THORN,** TOO! SHE DOESN'T HAVE ANY **IDEA** WHAT SHE'S UP AGAINST!

SHE'S COMPLETELY **VULNERABLE!**

I'LL SAY! THE LOCUSTS COULD MAKE HER BELIEVE **ANYTHING! HECK!** THEY COULD MAKE THE WHOLE **VALLEY** BELIEVE ANYTHING!

THAT'S IT! GRAB YOUR STUFF! WE HAVE TO GET BACK AND **WARN OUR FRIENDS!**

AYE, AYE, **CAP'N!**

YOU HEARD TH' MAN! LET'S **ROLL!**

YOU THERE! OPEN UP YOUR **MOUTH!**

WHY?

CHECKING FOR SMALL MAMMALS. ANYBODY IN THERE?

HELLO?

HELLO? HELLO?

OKAY, YER CLEAN!

C'MON, SMILEY! GET IT IN GEAR!

BUT, FONE BONE, THESE TWO CLOWNS CAN'T TAKE CARE OF A LITTLE **CUB!** THEY CAN'T EVEN TAKE CARE OF **THEMSELVES!**

BARTLEBY **CAN'T** LIVE IN THE VALLEY, SMILEY! HE WON'T BE **SAFE!**

SAY! SPEAKING OF **THE VALLEY--** LOOK OUT THERE!

WHAT?

THAT COLUMN OF SMOKE WE SAW IS **GONE!** DO YOU THINK TH' FOREST FIRE IS OUT?

I GUESS SO. BUT I'M NOT SO SURE IT **WAS** A FOREST FIRE . . .

WHAT ELSE COULD IT HAVE BEEN?

I DON'T KNOW FOR SURE, BUT ALL OF **ROCK JAW'S** TALK ABOUT **WAR** IS MAKING ME KIND OF **NERVOUS!**

ROCK JAW! THAT OL' **BLOWHARD!** HE WAS SO FULL OF HIMSELF...

... BUT WE SHOWED THAT GIANT KITTY CAT, **DIDN'T** WE, KIDS?

YEAH! HA! HA!

I BET HE'S **STILL** AT THE TOP OF THE **CLIFF** GUARDIN' THE ENTRANCE TO THAT **CAVE!**

HEE! HEE! OL' ROCK JAW DOESN'T KNOW ABOUT OUR **SECRET TUNNEL** DOWN THROUGH THE OLD **TEMPLE!**

LET'S NOT CONGRATULATE OURSELVES JUST YET.

BESIDES, SMILEY, I'M **MUCH** MORE WORRIED ABOUT WHAT MAY HAVE HAPPENED IN THE **VALLEY** WHILE WE WERE AWAY.

OKAY, OKAY. **STILL**, I'D LIKE TO SEE THAT OL' RASCAL'S **FACE** WHEN HE REALIZES WE GAVE HIM TH' **SLIP!**

MR. BONE, IF YOU'RE WORRIED THAT SOMETHING MAY HAVE **HAPPENED** WHILE WE WERE GONE, WHY DON'T YOU ASK THE TWO **RATS** WE HAVE WITH US?

GOOD IDEA.

HEY, **YOU TWO!** WHAT DO YOU KNOW ABOUT THOSE COLUMNS OF **SMOKE** WE SAW DOWN IN THE VALLEY?

WE KNOW **NOTHING!** WE ARE ONLY LOWLY FOOT SOLDIERS ON **BORDER PATROL!**

BORDER PATROL?! THE FIRST TIME I **MET** YOU WAS ON THE OTHER SIDE OF THE VALLEY! YOU WERE DEEP IN **DRAGON TERRITORY!**

YES, YESSS, WE WERE BREAKING THE **TREATY**-- BUT **KINGDOK** COMMANDED US TO **DO IT!**

KINGDOK'S ADVISOR, **THE HOODED ONE,** TOLD HIM THAT A NEW **LEADER** WAS ENTERING THE VALLEY -- A LEADER WHO BORE A **STAR** ON HIS CHEST!

KINGDOK SENT US ACROSS THE VALLEY TO THE **DRAGON'S STAIR** TO **CAPTURE** THIS **UPSTART THREAT!**

THAT'S RIDICULOUS! OUR COUSIN **PHONEY BONE** IS NO LEADER! I CAN'T IMAGINE WHAT GAVE YOU GUYS THE IDEA HE WAS A **THREAT!**

ARE YOU SURE KINGDOK DIDN'T HAVE **OTHER** REASONS FOR SENDING YOU ACROSS THE VALLEY AND VIOLATING THE **TREATY?**

KINGDOK HATES THE FLAT-LANDERS, IT'S **TRUE,** BUT THE TIME WAS NOT SO LONG AGO THAT HE WAS CONTENT TO ABIDE BY THE TREATY AND LEAVE THE VALLEY DWELLERS ALONE ...

ALL THAT CHANGED WHEN THE **HOODED ONE** ARRIVED... HE CAME TO US FROM THE VALLEY... ONE OF THE WANDERING HOLY MEN KNOWN AS **STICK-EATERS**...

...AND WITH HIM CAME THE LOCUSTS AND THE **DREAMS!**

THE POWER OF THE LOCUSTS IS **VERY STRONG!**

YOU SAW IT TODAY AT THE OLD **TEMPLE!** THE DREAMS CAN MAKE YOU BELIEVE THE SKY **ITSELF** IS FALLING!

WITHOUT THE HOODED ONE TO **CONTROL** THE LOCUSTS, WE MIGHT ALL BE ROLLING SENSLESSLY ON THE GROUND, **MAD AS LOONS!**

CRIPES!

HMM.

MORE AND MORE KINGDOK **LISTENS** TO THIS STICK-EATER AND HIS LOCUSTS.

TO THE POINT THAT KINGDOK MUST **OBEY** THE HOODED ONE FOR **FEAR** THAT THE LOCUST WILL **OVERWHELM HIM!**

WE **ALL MUST** OBEY!

AND **THIS** IS THE KIND OF LIFE YOU WANT TO SEND LITTLE **BARTLEBY** BACK TO? SOME KIND OF **INSECT CULT?**

BARTLEBY IS A **RAT CREATURE**, SMILEY! IF THIS IS WHAT RAT CREATURES **BELIEVE**, THEN WHO ARE WE TO JUDGE?

IT WAS NOT ALWAYS SO. IN THE OLD DAYS THE **HUM-HUM** WAS GOOD. WE WERE HAPPY.

NOW WITH THE COMING OF THE **LOCUSTS**, IT IS DIFFICULT TO TELL WHAT IS GOOD, OR WHAT IS **REAL**.

THE HOODED ONE BLAMES OUR UNHAPPINESS ON THE **VALLEY PEOPLE** AND **THE DRAGONS**, AND ON THE **TREATY** WHICH FORCES US TO LIVE IN THE MOUNTAINS.

HE SAYS WE MUST RETURN TO THE **OLD WAYS**... TO THE TIME BEFORE THERE **WERE** VALLEY PEOPLE... WHEN THERE WAS **ORDER** IN THE WORLD.

YOU DON'T HAVE TO **LISTEN** TO THE HOODED ONE.

THAT'S RIGHT, HE'S NOT EVEN **ONE** OF YOU! IF YOU ASK ME, HIS **MOTIVES** ARE PRETTY **SUSPECT!**

IF WE DO **NOT** LISTEN TO HIM... HOW WILL WE BE HAPPY?

ONLY WHEN YOU TRULY **UNDERSTAND** THE HOODED ONE'S MOTIVES WILL YOU LEARN THE **MEANING OF** HAPPINESS...

WHO...?

YOU SEE, HAPPINESS **ITSELF** IS JUST AN EMOTION THAT CAN BE **INDUCED** . . .

THE ONLY THING OF **SUBSTANCE** THAT MATTERS IS **POWER!**

WHAT ABOUT **GOOD** AND **EVIL?**

BAH! THERE IS NO GOOD AND EVIL. WHAT IS EVIL TO **YOU** DEPENDS ON WHAT **SIDE** YOU ARE ON. WHAT IS **GOOD** TO YOU IS EVIL TO THE **RAT CREATURES**, AND VICE VERSA.

THAT'S NOT **TRUE!**

ISN'T IT, MY LITTLE ORPHAN? DO YOU THINK THE **SUN** CARES IF YOUR MOMMA AND POPPA WERE **EATEN** BY RAT CREATURES? IT DOESN'T.

THE SUN WILL **SET** TONIGHT AND **RISE AGAIN** TOMORROW WHETHER YOU AND I ARE HERE OR NOT.

ANYTHING **THESE** MISERABLE WRETCHES DO IS **UTTERLY** INSIGNIFICANT.

THERE IS NO GOOD OR EVIL. . . ONLY **NATURE.** AND IN NATURE, THE ONLY THING THAT MATTERS IS **POWER!**

ONCE WE CROSS THIS PLATEAU AND START UP THAT **PATH**, WE WON'T GET ANOTHER CHANCE TO **ESCAPE!**

THIS IS IT, HUH?

WHAT'RE WE GONNA **DO?!**

YOU'RE **WRONG**, MR. ROCK JAW! THERE'S OTHER STUFF THAT **MATTERS!** LIKE FRIENDSHIP AND **TRUST!**

TAKE IT EASY, RODERICK! DON'T LET THAT **BULLY** GET TO YOU!

FRIENDSHIP AND TRUST ARE MERELY **EARTHBOUND** SENTIMENTS THAT ONLY LEAD TO TROUBLE. TRUST **NO ONE**, THAT'S **MY** MOTTO.

THE LIGHT WILL BE GONE SOON. IF WE CAN STALL HIM, WE MIGHT HAVE A CHANCE TO MAKE A BREAK IN THE DARK!

RIGHT!

UH, OH! HEADS UP!

OUR ESCAPE PLAN JUST GOT COMPLICATED!

UH, OH.

HE NEVER CAME DOWN!

C'MON! SOMETHING HAPPENED!

SMILEY! DON'T--!

BE CAREFUL! THERE'S GONNA BE RAT CREATURES ALL OVER THE PLACE!

THAT'S WEIRD... IT'S AWFUL QUIET.

LET'S PEEK OUT.

!

THERE'S NOBODY HERE!

THERE HE IS!

WHAT'S HE DOIN'?!

HE'S TRYING TO REJOIN THE GROUP, TOO!

BUT I DON'T WANT HIM TO REJOIN TH' GROUP!

IT'S WHERE HE BELONGS, SMILEY! IT'S WHAT HE WANTS TO DO!

MMMMMM.

DON'T BE SAD! IT'S WHAT WE CAME HERE TO DO! THIS IS A HAPPY ENDING!

NATURE HAS TAKEN ITS COURSE!

WILL HE BE OKAY?

YEAH. YEAH. HE'LL BE FINE.

LISTEN . . .

YOU CAN WATCH HIM FOR A WHILE IF YOU WANT, BUT NOT TOO LONG -- WE GOTTA GO, ALL RIGHT?

I GUESS.

GOOD-BYE, BARTLEBY.

I GOTTA GO NOW.

...TO BE CONTINUED.

About JEFF SMITH

JEFF SMITH was born and raised in the American Midwest and learned about cartooning from comic strips, comic books, and watching animated shorts on TV. After four years of drawing comic strips for The Ohio State University's student newspaper and co-founding Character Builders animation studio in 1986, Smith launched the comic book *BONE* in 1991. Between *BONE* and other comics projects, Smith spends much of his time on the international guest circuit promoting comics and the art of graphic novels.

More about BONE

An instant classic when it first appeared in the U.S. as an underground comic book in 1991, Bone has since garnered 38 international awards and sold a million copies in 15 languages. Now, Scholastic's GRAPHIX imprint is publishing full-color graphic novel editions of the nine-book *BONE* series. Look for the continuing adventures of the Bone cousins in *Old Man's Cave*.